THE
SPEAKING FROM THE HEART
WORKBOOK

A PRACTICAL GUIDE
TO THE
MODERN LOVE LANGUAGES

ANNE HODDER-SHIPP, CSE

SHOEBOX PRESS

welcome

If you're looking at this, it's probably because you read or heard about my ebook, *Speaking from the Heart: 18 Languages for Modern Love,* and felt inspired to do something extra with it. I'm honored! I made this workbook as a complement to the ebook and to provide a tangible tool that readers can use while they swipe or scroll through it.

The worksheets in this workbook contain original exercises I created and have used over the last 5 years facilitating individual and group workshops throughout Los Angeles. I paid attention to what clients did and didn't connect with and noticed what needed to be updated and expanded. Much like I did with the original love language concept!

Some of the activities may feel familiar, some might feel new, and others might just feel weird. Give them a chance. Test them out and see if they might give you a little more insight or perspective on how you relate to love. Or don't! No one will know.

As always, thank you for your support and for trusting me with this work. See you on the Internet!

Hi!
I'm Anne.

That's me in my office.

I am a white, queer femme based in Portland, OR, and I have worked in the sexuality field since 2007. You can learn more about my background and training at my website at the bottom of this page.

There's a lot to know about me, but the 1st and possibly most important thing to keep in mind is that **I don't have it all figured out.** I'm navigating life and relationships just like you probably are, and I'm flailing and stumbling along the way. And that's OK!

SOME FACTS ABOUT ME:

1   I love cats

2   I have a twin sister

3   I have misophonia

4   My sun sign is Gemini

5   My fave movie is Amélie

6   I'm allergic to pork

SPEAKING FROM THE HEART: 18 LANGUAGES FOR MODERN LOVE

1,300+ COPIES SOLD!

This is the ebook that started it all! *Speaking from the Heart: 18 Languages for Modern Love* was officially released on April 2, 2021 (my mom's 70th birthday). Since then, more than 1,300 copies have been purchased from my website, plus hundreds more from book stores online. Clearly, I wasn't the only one waiting for an expansive update to the love languages!

SPEAKING FROM THE HEART

18 LANGUAGES
FOR
MODERN
LOVE

AN UPDATED & EXPANSIVE APPROACH

FEATURED IN:

♡ 10+ podcasts

♡ 5 viral social posts

♡ 3 exclusive workshops

♡ 1 keynote

♡ 3 judgy reviews (lol)

IMPORTANT ACKNOWLEDGEMENTS!

Collaboration and community is a key part of my life and work. The people listed below have played important roles in my life, including helping me become a better person or professional, or supporting the success of the Modern Love Languages. Please check out their work, buy their books or courses, revel in their brilliance, and tell your friends!

NATHANIEL HODDER-SHIPP

ELLE CHASE

SANDRA ANN MILLER

SARAH TOMCHESSON

DR. GRACE ABRUZZO

DR. BIANCA LAUREANO

KAMI ORANGE

KEZIA VIDA

DR. EMILY NAGOSKI

ADRIENNE MAREE BROWN

BELL HOOKS

DR. JULIA B. COLWELL

SONYA RENEE TAYLOR

ESTHER PEREL

Plus a HUGE thanks to everyone who's taken the time to post or comment about my work on social media.

Word of mouth is powerful!

ABOUT
MODERN LOVE LANGUAGES

Speaking from the Heart: 18 Languages for Modern Love
and the Modern Love Languages framework centers all
experiences and expressions of love, represents humans
and relationships of all kinds, and encourages readers
to consider expanding their definition and
understanding of love to encompass more than
romance or family relations. It also offers 18 different
examples of ways people can show, receive, and
experience love to assist in that journey.

If you haven't yet, please read *Speaking from the Heart:*
18 Languages for Modern Love before using this
workbook. This modern and expansive update to the
concept of love languages is drastically and
intentionally different, and the exercises in this
workbook are created specifically to be completed
using the Modern Love Languages approach.

OK? OK! Let's get started!

ABOUT
THIS WORKBOOK

This workbook is a mix of tools and exercises designed to help you explore your relationship to love. They will help you cut through the biases, negative self-talk, assumptions, rules, and conditioning you are holding onto that's potentially getting in your way.

Think of this work as exploratory. You're gathering useful information about yourself. There's nothing about what you find or learn that deserves criticism or judgment.

You don't have to *do* anything with what you find or learn, either. Sometimes, we just want to take a peek and see what's there, and then go back to our regularly scheduled programming. Other times, we want to take what we discover and use it to disrupt that programming and change the figurative channel. However you choose to use this workbook, there's no "correct" way to do it, so take the pressure off!

SOMETHING ELSE
ABOUT THIS WORKBOOK

The exercises and activities in this workbook are put in an intentional order. Each one acts like a brick to support the next one, building up to a series of exercises that are specific to the Modern Love Languages.

By the end of this workbook, after completing each exercise, you should have enough insight and information about yourself and your experience of love in order to confidently identify what Modern Love Languages resonate with you the most.

This doesn't mean the exercises and worksheets can't be done on their own or in a different order, and certainly doesn't mean you can't just skip right to the end. You do you! Make this process your own! Create your own workbook adventure! Whatever it takes to do the work, do it. Nobody knows you better than you.

HOW TO USE THIS WORKBOOK

Some helpful "do's" to keep in mind:

DO Stay curious and open-minded.

DO Skip the worksheets or exercises you don't find useful or applicable.

DO Prepare to think about feelings and relationships that might feel raw or painful.

DO Notice what you're feeling during each exercise. Maybe even journal about it.

DO Use the notes section (pages 80-83) to write down ideas or thoughts as they come up.

DO Take your time.

DO Take what you need and leave the rest.

HOW <u>NOT</u> TO USE THIS WORKBOOK

Some important "don'ts" to keep in mind:

 Use this workbook when you're feeling upset, distracted, or angry.

 Put pressure on yourself. No one will see this but you!

 Overthink it.

 Judge or criticize yourself or your feelings.

 Force anything. You can always skip it or come back to it later.

 Rush it.

 Skip the "feel your feelings" part.

A NOTE
ABOUT ATTRIBUTION

If you feel inspired by any of these exercises or worksheets and want to use them in your own workplace, community groups, professional practice, fellowship, or for someone other than yourself, I would greatly appreciate it if you would please credit me and this workbook, as well as any names mentioned alongside the activity. Maybe even provide them with website or social media links, too!

You do not have permission to profit from re-creating or re-printing anything you find in this workbook, or to pass anything you found here as your own.

You can find my formal copyright notice at the beginning of this workbook.

I choose to trust that you, dear reader, will do the right thing.

A NOTE
ABOUT ACCESSIBILITY

Throughout this workbook, you will notice discussion of accessibility. Accessibility can mean different things to different people, and it can show up in many ways.

This workbook treats accessibility as an essential part of the learning and growing process. On these pages, it shows up in several forms, including:

- Providing options, choices, modifications, and alternatives within the worksheets
- Making space for multiple knowledge and experience levels
- Representation of a variety of experiences
- Clear and transparent instructions
- Examples of responses to get you started
- Large-sized fonts and high-contrast grayscale
- Providing permission and reminders for the reader to self-identify and self-guide their process

MORE
ABOUT ACCESSIBILITY

It is important to acknowledge that many resources about love and relationships that are popular and available today are not as accessible as they could be. It doesn't mean they aren't effective or helpful! It does mean, though, that they don't always effectively represent the wide variety, complexity, and nuanced nature of love and how our identities and life experiences impact the way we relate to it. Love is not one-size-fits-all and cannot be taught or discussed as though it is a standard part of being human.

Many people (myself included) have felt left out or dismissed by many of these resources. My intention with the Modern Love Languages is to disrupt this by discussing love and providing guidance using an expansive lens that acknowledges the wisdom and expertise that is already within each of us. A big part of my job is to simply help bring it to the surface.

GLOSSARY: WHAT DOES THAT WORD MEAN?

Below and on the next two pages are explanations of some words and phrases you will see used throughout this workbook, so we can be on the same page!

ACCESSIBILITY: Typically means making something easier or more equitable to do, understand, appreciate, enjoy, participate in, or generally have access to.

ALLYSHIP: Typically describes actions that a person with power or privilege of any kind chooses to take to recognize and/or unlearn biases or prejudice and show support for groups impacted by systems of oppression (like racism, transphobia, sexism, ageism, homophobia, fatphobia, ableism, and more). Allyship or being an ally is not an identity. It is an ongoing practice, not an identity, and something one must consistently and intentionally maintain.

WHAT DOES THAT WORD MEAN?

Here are explanations of some more words and phrases you will see used throughout this workbook, so we can be on the same page!

EXPANSIVENESS: Typically means recognizing and affirming all the unique and nuanced ways humans identify, relate (or don't relate) to other people, engage (or don't engage) with the world, feel (or don't feel) emotions, make choices, and experience life without comparing them to a baseline or default norm. Expansiveness also rejects the assumption that there is a baseline or default norm to begin with.

OPPRESSION: In this context, the active discrimination, control, or prejudice that individuals or groups with power hold over others. It can show up in many ways, including limiting access to freedoms, resources, healthcare, education, safety, housing, employment, community, personal beliefs, self-expression, and even joy.

WHAT DOES THAT WORD MEAN?

Here are explanations of some more words and phrases you will see used throughout this workbook, so we can be on the same page!

POWER: Power can take many forms. In this context, power includes an individual (like you), an institution (like government), or group (like billionaires) having authority, influence, and/or control over other people's decisions, resources, experiences, permissions, safety, community, knowledge, information, education, access, and other important parts of life, and sometimes whether they are even available.

PRIVILEGE: Typically describes any advantage, benefit, or access to power or safety that is uniquely available to certain groups and not available to others. It does not mean an absence of pain, difficulties, discrimination, or other challenges, but that the challenges they DO face are not related to the privilege they have.

THE 18 MODERN LOVE LANGUAGES!

1. ACCOUNTABILITY
2. ACTIVE LISTENING
3. ACTS OF EMPATHY
4. AFFIRMING COMMUNICATION
5. BESTOWING
6. EMOTIONAL LABOR
7. ENGAGED EXPERIENCES
8. INTENTIONAL TIME
9. PERSONAL GROWTH
10. PLATONIC TOUCH
11. PROBLEM-SOLVING
12. PROVIDING
13. SHARED BELIEFS
14. SOLIDARITY
15. TEAMWORK
16. THOUGHTFUL SERVICE
17. UNDIVIDED ATTENTION
18. UPSKILLING

PRO TIP:

Make a note of this page! It'll come in handy later in the workbook.

Have you read *Speaking from the Heart: 18 Languages for Modern Love* yet? These will make WAY more sense once you do.

"OUR FEELINGS ARE OUR MOST GENUINE PATHS TO KNOWLEDGE."

AUDRE LORDE

EMOTION WHEEL!

It can be hard to name what we're feeling sometimes, so use this emotion wheel to help you find the words. The next page has another one with even more emotion words.

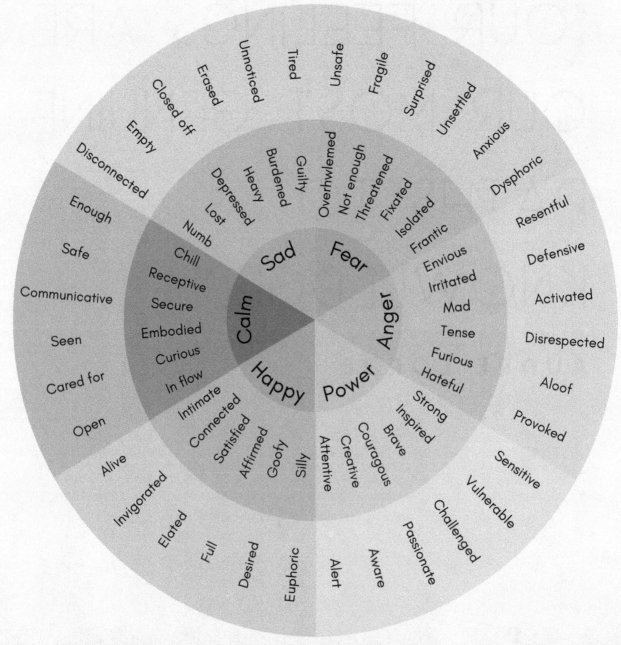

The original Feeling Wheel was created by Dr. Gloria Willcox in 1982!

EMOTION WHEEL!

Use your two emotion wheels anytime you need help naming what you're feeling - especially while you're completing this workbook!

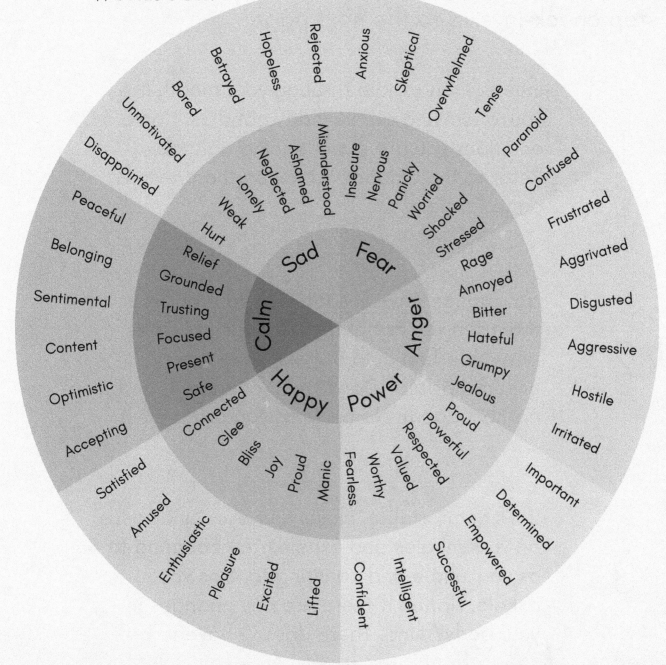

The original Feeling Wheel was created by Dr. Gloria Willcox in 1982!

LET'S CHECK IN!

Here is a 3-step check-in you can do before starting any of the exercises in this workbook — or anytime you're feeling upset. It involves breathing and body awareness, which means it's not accessible to everyone. For a more accessible 3-step check-in, skip to the next page.

1 Inhale, then exhale through your mouth like you're blowing out birthday candles. Name 3 emotions you are experiencing right now. Refer to the emotion wheel on the previous page for help!

2 Now notice any sensations in your body. Is there tension or tightness? Tingling? Does anywhere feel cold or hot? Painful or uncomfortable? Don't try to change it, and try not to judge it. Name what you are feeling.

3 If it's comfortable, close your eyes and focus on your inhales and exhales. Try counting to 4 as you inhale and counting to 4 as you exhale. Notice if there are any changes in your body/mind. There doesn't have to be!

ANOTHER CHECK IN!

Most grounding techniques require some kind of movement, breathing pattern, or body awareness, which makes them inaccessible to many people. Here is a more accessible option that can be used anytime you have intense emotions, feel frozen or anxious, or need to take your mind off something.

1 Wherever you are, take a moment to notice your surroundings using a sense you can access, like what you can see, feel, touch, smell, or hear.

2 Pick 1 thing that you notice from your surroundings. Name it and describe with as many details you can think of. What are the colors, textures, shapes, sizes, weight, scents, sounds, or other traits you notice?

3 For example, I touch my sweatpants. They feel soft with a little bumpy texture. I feel a long seam and a small hole on the left leg. They smell a little bit like coffee because I spilled some earlier.

"RADICAL SELF-LOVE DEMANDS THAT WE SEE OURSELVES AND OTHERS IN THE FULLNESS OF OUR COMPLEXITIES AND INTERSECTIONS AND THAT WE WORK TO CREATE SPACE FOR THOSE INTERSECTIONS."

SONYA RENEE TAYLOR

SHE/HER/WE

THE BODY IS NOT AN APOLOGY: THE POWER OF RADICAL SELF-LOVE

LET'S GET STARTED!

What do you think your Modern Love Languages are? All 18 are listed below. If you need a reminder about what they mean, refer to your ebook! Mark YES if you think it's one of your Modern Love Languages, NO if you don't, and MAYBE if you're not sure or "it depends."

This is just a starting point. The end of this workbook has a series of exercises designed to help you get clearer about which Modern Love Languages you most resonate with. You might be surprised by what you learn and discover along the way!

	YES	NO	MAYBE
ACCOUNTABILITY			
ACTIVE LISTENING			
ACTS OF EMPATHY			
AFFIRMING COMMUNICATION			
BESTOWING			
EMOTIONAL LABOR			

LET'S GET STARTED!

Continue marking YES if you think it's one of your Modern Love Languages, NO if you don't, and MAYBE if you're not sure or "it depends."

	YES	NO	MAYBE
ENGAGED EXPERIENCES			
INTENTIONAL TIME			
PERSONAL GROWTH			
PLATONIC TOUCH			
PROBLEM-SOLVING			
PROVIDING			
SHARED BELIEFS			
SOLIDARITY			
TEAMWORK			
THOUGHTFUL SERVICE			
UNDIVIDED ATTENTION			
UPSKILLING			

WHAT'S YOUR
MODERN LOVE LANGUAGE?

"Which one am I??" is one of the most common questions people ask me. There's a deep, understandable desire to have it all figured out and find some kind of peace in knowing which Modern Love Language is "me."

The tricky part is that I don't believe that anyone "is" one or more Modern Love Language. I believe that our experience of love is too nuanced and complex to be neatly and tidily identified and defined by a couple of keywords.

This isn't terribly convenient, I know, so this section is dedicated to help you get closer to understanding what Modern Love Languages mean to you.

As you complete this workbook, please remember to practice separating your understanding of love from your experiences of romance and sex, or lack thereof. Make space for Modern Love Languages to apply to and be present in ALL of your relationships.

WHAT'S IT TO YOU?

Let's first get clear about your hopes, intentions, and expectations with doing this work!

Q1 Why are Modern Love Languages important to you?

Q2 What do you hope to accomplish with this workbook?

Q3 How do you want to feel once you make it to the end?

WHAT'S IT TO YOU?

Next, let's get clear about YOUR definitions of the terms we've been exploring in this workbook:

Q1 What does "love" mean to you?

Q2 Why is love important to you? (Or is it?)

Q3 What is your favorite thing about love?

"THE GIVING OF LOVE IS AN EDUCATION IN ITSELF."

ELEANOR ROOSEVELT

WHAT IS LOVE?

We all have different relationships to the concept of love and how we most want to be loved by others. This is an exercise to help you get clear on what doesn't feel loving to you, even if it does for someone else.

Review the list below and on the next two pages. Anything that feels loving to you, put a **checkmark** or a mark of your choice in the star next to it. Anything that feels neutral or "it depends" to you, leave the star blank.

1. Hearing, "I love you." ☆
2. Making a chore chart together ☆
3. Having their hand on your knee while driving ☆
4. Being asked, "How can I help?" ☆
5. Having someone defend you online ☆
6. Getting a positive social media comment ☆
7. Knowing your cellphone number by heart ☆

WHAT IS LOVE?

Continue from the previous page:

8	Getting a gift you know they saved up for	☆
9	Being asked, "Will you teach me that?"	☆
10	Coming home to a clean apartment	☆
11	Apologizing to you after you call them out	☆
12	Hearing, "I get where you're coming from."	☆
13	Making eye contact when you're speaking	☆
14	Being sent memes, Reels, & TikToks	☆
15	Asking for personal space	☆
16	Canceling plans in order to hang with you	☆
17	Hello or goodbye kisses and/or hugs	☆
18	Going to a group meeting together	☆
19	Someone holding the door open for you	☆
20	Receiving a monthly allowance/stipend	☆

WHAT IS LOVE?

Continue from the previous page:

21 A caregiver asking permission to touch you ☆

22 Sharing own pronouns before asking for yours ☆

23 Hearing, "Let me get that for you." ☆

24 Making plans and handling logistics ☆

25 Learning about your disability or chronic illness ☆

26 Complimenting your physical strength ☆

27 A caregiver remembering your birthday ☆

28 Doing own research instead of asking you ☆

29 Hearing, "No problem!" when you have to cancel ☆

30 Being asked about your access needs ☆

 Take a minute to notice how you are feeling after going through this list. Did this feel easy or difficult? Did anything activate or irritate you? Did anything excite or inspire you?

WHAT IS LOVE?

Take this opportunity to fill in some of your own examples of words, actions, or other experiences that feel loving or like love.

I encourage you to FEEL into this exercise rather than think. Here's what I mean: you might avoid putting "buying me a present" on this list even though you feel cared for when you get a gift. That might be because you hold a judgment about gift-giving being shallow or that "love can't be bought."

If it feels loving to you, write it down - even if you feel a little judgy about it.

1

2

3

4

5

6

7

LET'S PROCESS AND REFLECT

Look at the examples on pages 29-31 that you marked as loving (with a checkmark or other mark), and respond to these questions:

Q1 Write the number(s) of each example:

Q2 Were you surprised by any of them? If yes, why?

Q3 Did you feel hesitant to mark any of them? Did you feel judgy about any? Why or why not?

LET'S PROCESS AND REFLECT MORE

Look at the examples on pages 29-31 with a star that you left blank because you felt neutral or "it depends." Respond to these questions:

Q1 Write the number(s) of each example:

Q2 Were you surprised to feel neutral about them? If yes, why?

Q3 Are there any contexts or situations in which any of the examples might actually feel loving? If yes, what are they?

"FEELINGS OR EMOTIONS ARE THE UNIVERSAL LANGUAGE & ARE TO BE HONORED. THEY ARE THE AUTHENTIC EXPRESSION OF WHO YOU ARE AT YOUR DEEPEST PLACE."

JUDITH WRIGHT

YOUR EXPERIENCE OF LOVE

What does it mean to you to feel loved? This is an activity designed to help you gain insight into your own unique experience of **receiving love**.

Think about at least five emotions that feel similar or related to what it's like for you to receive or experience love from someone else. Try looking at your emotion wheel on page 18 or 19 if you need help or inspiration!

For example, five emotions that I associate with feeling loved are: **noticed**, **safe**, **respected**, **valuable**, and **belonging**. Write yours below:

1. _____

2. _____

3. _____

4. _____

5. _____

Think of these as your "love words," the emotions that you most associate with feeling loved. **When you experience these emotions, you are connected to your experience of receiving love!**

YOUR EXPERIENCE OF LOVE

What does it feel like for you to love something or someone? This is an activity designed to help you gain insight into your own unique experience of **expressing love.**

Think about at least five emotions that feel similar or related to what it's like for you to communicate or show love toward someone else. Try looking at your emotion wheel on page 18 or 19 if you need help or inspiration!

For example, five emotions that I associate with giving love are: **in flow**, **connected**, **secure**, **trusting**, and **nurturing**. Write yours below:

1. _____

2. _____

3. _____

4. _____

5. _____

Think of these as your "loving words," the emotions that you most associate with expressing love. **When you experience these emotions, you are connected to your experience of giving or showing love!**

YOUR EXPERIENCE OF LOVE

What does it mean to you to NOT feel loved? This activity can help you get clearer about your experience of love by also thinking about what love doesn't feel like.

Think about at least five emotions that feel similar or related to what it's like when you don't feel loved by someone else. Try looking at your emotion wheel on page 18 or 19 if you need help!

For example, five emotions that I associate with feeling unloved are: **controlled**, **judged**, **disrespected**, **silenced**, and **ashamed**. Write yours below:

1._____

2._____

3._____

4._____

5._____

Think of these as your "hurt words," the emotions that you most associate with feeling unloved. **When you experience these emotions, you are disconnected to your experience of receiving love and one or more of your needs may not be getting met.**

LET'S DO ANOTHER CHECK-IN!

That last exercise might have left you feeling some type of way (use the emotion wheel on page 18 or 19 if you can't find the words). Here's another check-in that might help. It involves breathing and body awareness, so skip to the next page for another check-in option if needed. Show yourself some much-deserved care!

1 Inhale, then exhale through your mouth like you're blowing out birthday candles. Name 3 emotions you are experiencing right now. Say, "It makes sense I feel this way. There is nothing wrong with me."

2 Now notice any sensations in your body. Is there a part of your body that could use some attention? Rub your hands together for 10 seconds and place them on or near that area. Notice the pressure and temperature change.

3 If it's comfortable, close your eyes and notice how you are breathing. Try taking in more air with your inhales and notice how it feels for your chest to expand. It might hurt or feel tight. Breathe into the tension or back off if it doesn't feel good. You're in charge.

HERE'S ANOTHER ALTERNATIVE!

Try this grounding exercise as a way to orient or reorient yourself to the room or area you are in and engage various senses you have access to. This does not require movement, breathing a certain way, or much body awareness.

1 Wherever you are, take a moment to notice what you can see and/or feel around you. Count all of the things you see that are green, or count all of the things you feel that are textured or bumpy.

2 Now count all of the things you can hear around you. Try to identify what each sound is. Alternatively, count all of the things you can smell around you. Try to guess what each scent is.

3 Now name what you noticed. For example, "I see 7 green things. I feel 3 bumpy things. I hear birds, laughter, and a garbage truck. I smell grass, coffee, and lavender." Say this out loud or think it in your head, whichever feels more comfortable.

"I'VE LEARNED THAT PEOPLE WILL FORGET WHAT YOU SAID, PEOPLE WILL FORGET WHAT YOU DID, BUT PEOPLE WILL NEVER FORGET HOW YOU MADE THEM FEEL."

MAYA ANGELOU

YOUR EXPERIENCE OF LOVE

The inimitable bell hooks reminds us that, "Love is an action, never simply a feeling." This activity will help you think about the various behaviors we and others do that can communicate love.

First, let's think about the phrases we **say** to communicate love to others.

What I say when I'm having loving feelings (like what I listed on page 37) for someone:

1. *"I'm proud of you."*
2.
3.
4.
5.
6.

Could any of the phrases you wrote down be considered **Affirming Communication, Undivided Attention,** or **Active Listening?**

YOUR EXPERIENCE OF LOVE

Next, let's think about the actions we **do** to communicate love to others. What do you do **for** them, what do you do **with** them, and what do you **on your own** when you're feeling those feels?

What I do when I'm having loving feelings (like what I listed on page 37) for someone:

1. *DM them funny cat vids on TikTok*

2. _____

3. _____

4. _____

5. _____

6. _____

7. _____

 Could any of the actions you wrote down be considered **Thoughtful Service, Bestowing, Providing,** or **Platonic Touch?**

YOUR EXPERIENCE OF LOVE

Now, let's think about the phrases that **others say** that, to you, feels loving or like love.

Things people say that leave me feeling loved (or any feelings listed on page 36):

1. *"I know you're stressed, so I made dinner."*

2. _____

3. _____

4. _____

5. _____

6. _____

7. _____

Could any of the phrases you wrote down be considered **Accountability, Emotional Labor, Acts of Empathy, or Problem-solving?**

YOUR EXPERIENCE OF LOVE

Sometimes people say things that feel loving because they are actively fighting discrimination, calling in harm, acknowledging privilege, or showing allyship of some kind. This space is for those **phrases**.

Things people with power say that leave me feeling loved (or any feelings listed on page 36):

1. _"That's not a joke and it's not funny."_

2.

3.

4.

5.

6.

7.

 Could any of the phrases you wrote down be considered **Acts of Empathy, Emotional Labor, Problem-solving, or Solidarity?**

YOUR EXPERIENCE OF LOVE

Next, let's think about the actions **others do** that, to you, feel loving. What do they do **for** you, what do they do **with** you, and what else do they do that feels like love?

Things people do that leave me feeling loved (or any feelings listed on page 36):

1. *Have my cellphone number memorized.*

2. _____

3. _____

4. _____

5. _____

6. _____

7. _____

Could any of the actions you wrote down be considered **Engaged Experiences, Intentional Time, Solidarity,** or **Upskilling?**

YOUR EXPERIENCE OF LOVE

Now, let's think about the actions **others in power do** that, to you, feel loving. What do they do **for** you, what do they do **with** you, and what else do they do that communicates love?

Things people with power do that feel loving (or any feelings listed on page 36):

1. *Putting captions on Reels or TikTok videos.*

2. _____

3. _____

4. _____

5. _____

6. _____

7. _____

Could any of the actions you wrote down be considered **Accountability, Engaged Experiences, Intentional Time, Solidarity,** or **Upskilling?**

YOUR EXPERIENCE OF LOVE

Sometimes, it's easier to make a list of things that <u>don't</u> feel loving or like love than making a list of things that do. Take a moment to think about what **actions** might show up on your list:

Things people do that leave me feeling unloved (or any feelings on page 38):

1. *Leaving me out of the group chat.*

2. _____

3. _____

4. _____

5. _____

6. _____

7. _____

How did it feel to think about this?
Was it uncomfortable or painful?
Were you surprised by anything you wrote down?

YOUR EXPERIENCE OF LOVE

Sometimes, people with power or privilege do things that are meant to be an expression of love but, to us, don't feel loving at all and end up contributing to our experience of oppression. This space is for those **actions**.

Well-intended actions that leave me feeling unloved (or any feelings on page 38):

1. *Grabbing stuff out of my hands and carrying it.*

2. _____

3. _____

4. _____

5. _____

6. _____

7. _____

How did it feel to think about love from this perspective?

YOUR EXPERIENCE OF LOVE

Now, let's think about the **phrases** that others say that, to you, <u>don't</u> feel loving or like love.

Things people say that leave me feeling unloved (or any feelings listed on page 38):

1. _"You're super hot."_

2. _____

3. _____

4. _____

5. _____

6. _____

7. _____

How did it feel to write these down? Have you heard or been told any of these phrases before? Do you remember how you reacted or responded?

YOUR EXPERIENCE OF LOVE

Now, let's think about the **phrases** that others say that they think are loving but actually contribute to your experience of oppression and harm.

Well-intended phrases that leave me feeling unloved (or any feelings listed on page 38):

1. _"But you don't look disabled."_

2. _"I don't see race or color."_

3. _____

4. _____

5. _____

6. _____

7. _____

8. _____

 What emotions come up when you hear people say these phrases to you? How do you tend to react?

"SOMETIMES IT'S A FORM OF LOVE JUST TO TALK TO SOMEBODY THAT YOU HAVE NOTHING IN COMMON WITH AND STILL BE FASCINATED BY THEIR PRESENCE."

DAVID BYRNE

HE/HIM

WHAT'S YOUR MODERN LOVE LANGUAGE?

Look at the numbers you listed for Q1 on page 33 and match them with the Modern Love Languages listed below, and on the following pages. Notice that the examples of love from pages 29-31 can apply to more than just one! This is a way to start exploring which Modern Love Languages you resonate with:

1
- AFFIRMING COMMUNICATION
- EMOTIONAL LABOR

2
- ACCOUNTABILITY
- ENGAGED EXPERIENCES
- INTENTIONAL TIME
- PROBLEM-SOLVING
- TEAMWORK

3
- PLATONIC TOUCH
- ENGAGED EXPERIENCES

4
- AFFIRMING COMMUNICATION
- PROBLEM-SOLVING
- PROVIDING
- THOUGHTFUL SERVICE

WHAT'S YOUR
MODERN LOVE LANGUAGE?

5
- ACTS OF EMPATHY
- EMOTIONAL LABOR
- SOLIDARITY

6
- ACTS OF EMPATHY
- AFFIRMING COMMUNICATION
- SHARED BELIEFS
- SOLIDARITY

7
- SOLIDARITY
- THOUGHTFUL SERVICE

8
- BESTOWING
- PROVIDING
- THOUGHTFUL SERVICE

9
- AFFIRMING COMMUNICATION
- ENGAGED EXPERIENCES
- PERSONAL GROWTH
- UPSKILLING

10
- ACTS OF EMPATHY
- INTENTIONAL TIME
- PROVIDING
- THOUGHTFUL SERVICE

WHAT'S YOUR
MODERN LOVE LANGUAGE?

11
- AFFIRMING COMMUNICATION
- ACCOUNTABILITY

12
- ACTIVE LISTENING
- ACTS OF EMPATHY
- AFFIRMING COMMUNICATION
- EMOTIONAL LABOR
- SOLIDARITY

13
- ACTIVE LISTENING
- ENGAGED EXPERIENCES
- UNDIVIDED ATTENTION

14
- AFFIRMING COMMUNICATION
- BESTOWING
- PROVIDING

15
- ACCOUNTABILITY
- INTENTIONAL TIME
- PERSONAL GROWTH

16
- BESTOWING
- INTENTIONAL TIME
- THOUGHTFUL SERVICE

WHAT'S YOUR
MODERN LOVE LANGUAGE?

17
- ACTS OF EMPATHY
- AFFIRMING COMMUNICATION
- BESTOWING
- PLATONIC TOUCH

18
- ACCOUNTABILITY
- ENGAGED EXPERIENCES
- INTENTIONAL TIME
- SHARED BELIEFS
- SOLIDARITY
- TEAMWORK

19
- PROVIDING
- UNDIVIDED ATTENTION

20
- BESTOWING
- PROVIDING
- THOUGHTFUL SERVICE

21
- ACCOUNTABILITY
- ACTS OF EMPATHY
- AFFIRMING COMMUNICATION
- SOLIDARITY
- TEAMWORK
- THOUGHTFUL SERVICE

WHAT'S YOUR
MODERN LOVE LANGUAGE?

22
- ACTS OF EMPATHY
- AFFIRMING COMMUNICATION
- SOLIDARITY
- UNDIVIDED ATTENTION

23
- AFFIRMING COMMUNICATION
- BESTOWING
- PROBLEM-SOLVING
- PROVIDING
- THOUGHTFUL SERVICE

24
- EMOTIONAL LABOR
- PROBLEM-SOLVING
- PROVIDING
- THOUGHTFUL SERVICE

25
- ACCOUNTABILITY
- ACTS OF EMPATHY
- INTENTIONAL TIME
- PERSONAL GROWTH
- SOLIDARITY
- UPSKILLING

26
- AFFIRMING COMMUNICATION
- BESTOWING

WHAT'S YOUR
MODERN LOVE LANGUAGE?

27
- ACTS OF EMPATHY
- EMOTIONAL LABOR
- SOLIDARITY

28
- ACCOUNTABILITY
- PERSONAL GROWTH
- UPSKILLING

29
- AFFIRMING COMMUNICATION
- SHARED BELIEFS
- SOLIDARITY

30
- ACCOUNTABILITY
- ACTIVE LISTENING
- ACTS OF EMPATHY
- AFFIRMING COMMUNICATION
- SOLIDARITY

Did you notice how much overlap and flexibility there is here? That's because feeling love and feeling loved aren't rigid or strictly defined, and they often change or mean different things to us, depending on the relationship and the context.

There's no "right" or "wrong" here! If being given a compliment feels more like Bestowing than Affirming Communication, then so be it! You're the expert of your experience of love.

"TO TRULY LOVE WE MUST LEARN TO MIX VARIOUS INGREDIENTS - CARE, AFFECTION, RECOGNITION, RESPECT, COMMITMENT, AND TRUST, AS WELL AS HONEST AND OPEN COMMUNICATION."

bell hooks

ALL ABOUT LOVE: NEW VISIONS

WHAT'S YOUR
MODERN LOVE LANGUAGE?

Now that you've seen some specific examples of what the 18 Modern Love Languages can look, feel, or sound like, let's go even deeper to see which ones resonate with you the most.

Look at what you wrote down on page 42 – the **phrases you say** to express or communicate love. Which Modern Love Language(s) could they be examples of? For #1, I listed the Modern Love Languages that, to me, connect to the phrase I put for #1 on page 42. Please do the same for #2-#6!

1. *Affirming communication, acts of empathy.*

2. _____

3. _____

4. _____

5. _____

6. _____

WHAT'S YOUR
MODERN LOVE LANGUAGE?

Next, look at what you wrote down on page 43 - the **actions you do** to express or communicate love to others. Can you identify which Modern Love Language(s) they could be an example of? For #1, I listed the Modern Love Languages that, to me, connect to the action I put for #1 on page 43. Please do the same for #2-#7!

1. _Bestowing, providing, thoughtful service._

2. _____

3. _____

4. _____

5. _____

6. _____

7. _____

WHAT'S YOUR
MODERN LOVE LANGUAGE?

There is a good chance that the Modern Love Languages you listed on pages 60-61 are **the ones you use to express or communicate love to other people!**

Do you have any immediate thoughts or feelings after completing this part of the process? If so, please write them below:

WHAT'S YOUR
MODERN LOVE LANGUAGE?

Next, look at what you wrote down on page 44 - the **phrases others say** that feel loving to you. Can you identify which Modern Love Language(s) they could be an example of? For #1, I listed the Modern Love Languages that, to me, connect to the phrase I put for #1 on page 44. Please do the same for #2-#7!

1. Problem-solving, providing, solidarity, thoughtful service.

2.

3.

4.

5.

6.

7.

WHAT'S YOUR
MODERN LOVE LANGUAGE?

Notice what you wrote down on page 45 - the **phrases that people with power say** that feel loving. Are they examples of the same Modern Love Language(s) you listed on page 63? Are they different? For #1, I listed the Modern Love Languages that, to me, connect to the phrase I put for #1 on page 45. Please do the same for #2–#7!

1. _Acts of empathy, emotional labor, problem-solving, solidarity._

2. _____

3. _____

4. _____

5. _____

6. _____

7. _____

WHAT'S YOUR
MODERN LOVE LANGUAGE?

Now, look at what you wrote down on page 46 - **the actions others do** that feel loving to you. Can you identify which Modern Love Language(s) they could be an example of? For #1, I listed the Modern Love Languages that, to me, connect to the action I put for #1 on page 46. Please do the same for #2-#7!

1. _Acts of empathy, intentional time, thoughtful service._

2. _____

3. _____

4. _____

5. _____

6. _____

7. _____

WHAT'S YOUR
MODERN LOVE LANGUAGE?

Now, look at what you wrote down on page 47 – **the actions that people with power do** that feel loving to you. Are they examples of the same Modern Love Language(s) from page 65? Or are they different? For #1, I listed the Modern Love Languages that, to me, connect to the action I put for #1 on page 47. Please do the same for #2-#7!

1. _Accountability, providing, solidarity, thoughtful service._

2. _____

3. _____

4. _____

5. _____

6. _____

7. _____

WHAT'S YOUR
MODERN LOVE LANGUAGE?

There is a good chance that the Modern Love Languages you listed on pages 63-66 are **the ones that feel most loving when received from other people.**

Do you have any immediate thoughts or feelings after completing this part of the process? If so, please write them below:

YOUR EXPRESSION OF LOVE

Use this page as your go-to anytime you want to remember or reflect on your Modern Love Languages.

How I express or communicate love to others (pgs. 60-61):

How I receive love from others (pgs. 63-66):

"WHAT WE NEED RIGHT NOW IS A RADICAL, GLOBAL LOVE THAT GROWS FROM DEEP WITHIN US TO ENCOMPASS ALL LIFE."

adrienne maree brown

SHE/THEY

PLEASURE ACTIVISM: THE POLITICS OF FEELING GOOD

FINAL REFLECTION!

Go back to pages 23-24 and notice which Modern Love Languages you marked as YES, NO, and MAYBE. How do they compare to the Modern Love Languages you wrote on the previous page?

Which ones did you guess correctly?

Were any unexpected? What surprised you?

"LOVE MAKES YOUR SOUL CRAWL OUT FROM ITS HIDING PLACE."

ZORA NEALE HURSTON

ONE LAST CHECK-IN!

You have done SO much hard work and I'm excited for what comes next for you. It wouldn't feel right to say "bye" without some kind of closing, so let's do one last check-in. Skip to the next page for another check-in option!

1 Inhale through your nose and exhale through your mouth like you're blowing out birthday candles. Skip this part if breathing isn't accessible right now. Name 3 emotions you are now experiencing.

2 Think of 3 people, places, animals, or items that you feel grateful for. Say each out loud followed by, "Thank you for being in my life. I love you."

3 Find a mirror or reflection and look at yourself, as much as is comfortable. Make eye contact with yourself and say, "I am lovable and I deserve to feel loved."

ANOTHER CHECK-IN OPTION!

This check-in involves using a positive memory to tap into feelings and sensations that feel comfortable, grounding, or even safe to you. It does not require movement, breathing a certain way, or much body awareness.

1 If comfortable, close your eyes. If not, keep them open. Think about a time when you felt a deep sense of joy. It can be a childhood memory or even something that just happened yesterday!

2 Tap into that memory as much as you can. Do you remember what you were wearing? Who was around you? What was the temperature? What could you see or hear? Spend a moment in this memory.

3 Notice if the emotions you were feeling before this check-in are still there, or if they have changed in any way. When you feel ready, open your eyes if they were closed. Give yourself gratitude for taking care of yourself.

"YOU ARE LOVED,
YOU DESERVE LOVE,
YOU ARE WORTHY
OF LOVE, AND
THAT'S THE TRUTH."

JEFFREY MARSH

THEY/THEM

YOU MADE IT TO
THE END!

I HOPE YOU FEEL
PROUD OF
YOURSELF.

I FEEL PROUD OF YOU!

YOUR MODERN LOVE LANGUAGE JOURNEY DOESN'T HAVE TO END HERE!

This workbook is just the beginning! If you found this Modern Love Language workbook helpful and are ready to dig deeper into your relationship with love, sign up for my email list or send me a message!

ANNEHODDERSHIPP.COM/CONTACTME

You'll be first to know about **new Modern Love Languages products** PLUS **the Modern Love Language Intensive**, an online weekend workshop guided by yours truly!

If you haven't already, don't forget to check out *Speaking from the Heart: 18 Languages for Modern Love* – the groundbreaking ebook that started it all!

www.themodernlovelanguages.com

LOOKING FOR MORE PROFESSIONAL & PERSONAL DEVELOPMENT LIKE THIS?

If you enjoyed or felt inspired by the activities & exercises in this workbook, you might enjoy my other heart-centered offerings! Check them out:

 Live & recorded courses that help you find more pleasure & joy. www.s3xplus.com

 Compassionate sex education & professional development. www.everyonedeservessexed.com

Private coaching for people & couples, plus dreamwork. www.annehoddershipp.com

WANT TO WORK WITH ME?

15%
DISCOUNT

This coupon can be used to book a private virtual coaching, dreamwork, or professional development session with Anne.

https://bit.ly/hireanne

Use code: MLLWORKBOOK

CHEERS!

FIND ME ON SOCIAL

@theannehodder

NOTES

NOTES

NOTES

NOTES

Printed in the USA
CPSIA information can be obtained
at www.ICGtesting.com
LVHW012107021123
762921LV00015B/113